Cello Exam Pieces

ABRSM Grade 2

Selected from the 2020–2023 syllabus

Name

Date of exam

GW00538490

Contents

Cello consultant: Anita Strevens
Footnotes: Anthony Burton

Other pieces for Grade 2   DUET *with cello accompaniment*   PF/VC *with piano or cello accompaniment*

First published in 2019 by ABRSM (Publishing) Ltd,
a wholly owned subsidiary of ABRSM, 4 London Wall Place,
London EC2Y 5AU, United Kingdom
© 2019 by The Associated Board of the Royal Schools of Music
Distributed worldwide by Oxford University Press

Music origination by Julia Bovee
Cover by Kate Benjamin & Andy Potts, with thanks to Brighton College
Printed in England by Page Bros (Norwich) Ltd, on materials from
sustainable sources.

Minuet

from *The Fiddler's Nursery*

Transcribed by Wendy Max

Adam Carse
(1878–1958)

Adam Carse was an English composer who specialised in music for young performers. He taught harmony and counterpoint at the Royal Academy of Music in London for nearly 20 years, and was a writer on the history of the orchestra and of orchestral instruments. He adopted the form of the minuet, a dance popular in the 18th century, for this piece in his collection *The Fiddler's Nursery*, for violin and piano. It was adapted for cello by Wendy Max.

Come, ye Sons of Art

A:2

Arranged by Catherine Black
and Paul Harris

Henry Purcell
(1659–95)

As part of his duties as composer for the English court, the 17th-century composer Henry Purcell wrote many 'odes' to mark notable occasions in the lives of the royal family. His ode *Come, ye Sons of Art* was a celebration of the birthday of the music-loving Queen Mary II in April 1694. After an orchestral overture, the first section consists of the same music performed three times, by the orchestra, solo alto voice and chorus: this arrangement presents it twice. The words are:

> Come, come, ye Sons of Art, come, come away.
> Tune all your voices and instruments play
> To celebrate, to celebrate this triumphant day.

Parson's Farewell

from *The English Dancing Master*

Arranged by David Blackwell

Trad. English

The English Dancing Master is a collection of more than 500 traditional fiddle tunes for country dancing. It was published in London by John Playford and his heirs in successive editions between 1651 and about 1728. 'Parson's Farewell' is a dance for couples, which was included, with instructions to the dancers, in the first edition. Earlier versions of the tune can be found in various manuscript and printed sources in the Netherlands, France and Germany; in several of these it is described as a bourrée.

As long as he needs me

from *Oliver!*

Arranged by Nikki Iles

B:1

Lionel Bart
(1930–99)

Oliver! is a musical, with words and music by Lionel Bart, based on the novel *Oliver Twist* by Charles Dickens. It had its first, highly successful run in the West End of London from 1960, and has been revived frequently ever since. The central character, Oliver, is a poor young London boy who becomes a member of a criminal gang led by Fagin. He is protected by Nancy, an older member of the gang. She is mistreated by her boyfriend, fellow gang member Bill Sikes. But she declares her belief in their continuing love in the song 'As long as he needs me'.

B:2

Ballade

No. 7 from *Eight Very Easy Pieces*

Ludwig Lebell
(1872/3–1954)

Ludwig Lebell was born in Austria, and is said to have studied at the Vienna Conservatoire with the composer Anton Bruckner and the cellist David Popper. He settled in London, where he taught the cello and coached chamber music at Trinity College of Music for the last 40 years of his life. He published studies and many shorter pieces for young cellists, including in 1921 a set of *Eight Very Easy Pieces*. The title of the seventh piece, 'Ballade', refers to the resemblance of the melody to a folk song, and suggests the telling of a story.

Down by the salley gardens

B:3

Arranged by Alan Bullard

Trad. Irish

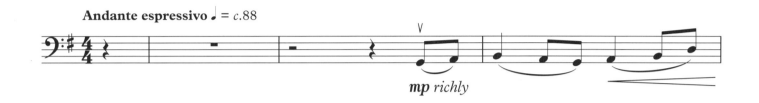

The words of the song 'Down by the salley gardens' are an 1889 poem by the famous Irish writer W. B. Yeats. Yeats originally called his poem 'An Old Song Re-Sung', describing it as 'an attempt to reconstruct an old song from three lines imperfectly remembered by an old peasant woman in the village of Ballisodare, Sligo, who often sings them to herself'. The 'salley gardens' of the first line are a plantation of willow trees, where a young man meets his girlfriend. The words are usually sung to the traditional Irish melody *The Moorlough Shore*, arranged by Herbert Hughes. This is the version arranged here.

The Flintstones

Arranged by Nikki Iles

Words and music by Joseph Barbera (1911-2006), William Hanna (1910-2001) and Hoyt Curtin (1922-2000)

The Flintstones was a cartoon series shown on American television from 1960 to 1966, and in re-runs and revivals after that, which became popular in many countries. It was set in the Stone Age, but featured a family behaving like a modern family. From 1962 to 1966, its opening and closing music was the song 'Flintstones, meet the Flintstones'. This was written by the musical director of the Hanna-Barbera animation studio, Hoyt S. Curtin, in collaboration with Joseph Barbera and William Hanna.

Allegro

No. 2 from *Two Pieces*

C:2

Mihály Hajdu
(1909–90)

Mihály Hajdu was a Hungarian composer and teacher. He studied composition with Zoltán Kodály at the Budapest Academy of Music, where he later became a professor of music theory and folk music. His compositions include an opera, orchestral works, chamber music, and many publications for young performers. Among these are *Two Pieces* for cello and piano, of which this rhythmic dance is the second.

The composer gives the option to play the cello notes in the final bar an octave lower. Students should play the printed version in an exam.

Staten Island

Arranged by Alan Bullard

Trad. Irish

'Staten Island' is a traditional Irish hornpipe, a fiddle tune for dancing. It first appeared in print in 1782, in the second volume of James Aird's *A Selection of Scotch, English, Irish, and Foreign Airs*, published in Glasgow. Staten Island is a borough of the city of New York, linked to Manhattan by a famous ferry. The tune may have been given the name while British troops were stationed there during the American War of Independence.